Erotic fantasies

Brilliant ideas for raunchy role play

BODY
LIPS
BLOW

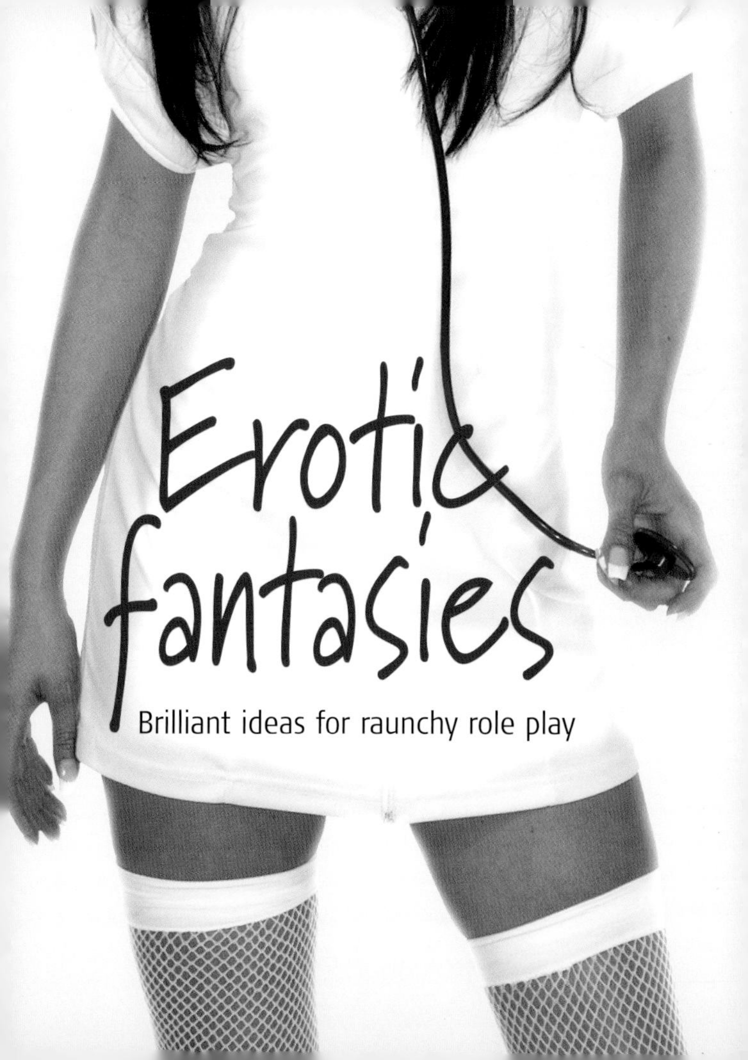
Erotic fantasies
Brilliant ideas for raunchy role play

Careful now
The tips for revving up your sex life contained in this book are all tried and tested winners. We hope you (and your partner) have a great time and enjoy developing your fantasy life, but please do think before you act. We can't be held responsible for any arguments or other fallout resulting from using the tips in this book. Please make sure that your partner is happy with any plans before you go ahead, start gently if you're not sure, and remember that sex in public places is illegal. Have fun and play safe.

Infinite ideas would like to thank Helena Frith Powell, Marcelle Perks and Elisabeth Wilson for their contributions to this book.

First published in 2006 by
The Infinite Ideas Company Limited
36 St Giles
Oxford, OX1 3LD
United Kingdom
www.infideas.com

A CIP catalogue record for this book is available from the British Library

ISBN 10: 1-904902-91-X
ISBN 13: 978-1-904902-91-1

Designed and typeset by Baseline Arts Ltd, Oxford
Printed in Singapore

Brilliant ideas

'I have too many fantasies to be a housewife. I guess I am a fantasy.'

MARILYN MONROE

Introduction

Somebody once said that sexual fantasy was the 'thinking man's television', and they weren't kidding. Hours of entertainment and you don't even have to leave your sofa to enjoy it. If you get up off your butt and take your fantasies into the bedroom, they'll give you explosive orgasms too. What goes on in your mind is as important as what's going on around your genitals. However, just like talking dirty, it has to be your own 'script'. Many people read the lists of top male fantasies or top female fantasies (usually both headed by lesbian sex) and don't believe it. If you're a woman who thinks about two girls getting stuck in and this drives you over the edge, terrific. But if it doesn't, you shouldn't give up finding out what does. Men tend to have more access to porn, and that hotwires their fantasies and preferences pretty early on. Women don't usually have this advantage. But bear with us. Even if sexual fantasy isn't a big part of your life right now, it's a habit well worth getting into.

Sexual fantasy increases your libido. The more you think about sex, the more you want it. Plus, just a glimmer of the thought of your fantasy during sex will increase your pleasure a hundred-fold and if you're a woman it'll make orgasm faster (if you're a bloke, more enjoyable).

Your fantasy can be filled with people you know really well or people you glimpsed on a bus twenty years ago, and again they can be idealised versions – more exciting, demanding, inventive. Think in detail. Tell yourself these stories while masturbating. Imagine hands grasping, tongues licking, words being whispered. (You don't need the whole story when you're having sex, just a flash of detailed scene.) It takes practice – you'll enjoy it!

Once you've discovered fantasyland, up the dirtiness quotient. The true power of fantasy lies in forbidden thoughts, so try thinking of some real extremes. Remember, this has nothing to do with who you are in real life.

1

Dirty dancing

Dancing is described as the vertical expression of a horizontal desire. And we automatically assume that a good dancer is a good lover.

There is nothing quite as sexy as someone who dances well so why not build some sexy moves into your fantasy. Here's how to turn striptease fantasy into reality and become a lap dancer – in the privacy of your own home. It's easy to learn how. Have a search for online tips or rent movies featuring stripping such as Striptease and Showgirls. It's fairly straightforward though: just dance seductively wearing very little while your partner/audience stuffs cash into your g-string;

sexy, fun and profitable. Some exercise classes now use pole dancing as a way to fitness. Check out 'Polestars' for a course near you; they have a great website (www.polestars.net).

So how do you become a sexy dancer? It has a lot to do with rhythm. And relaxing. Here are a few basic dos and don'ts:

- Relax; let the rhythm flow over you, there is nothing worse than a tense dancer.
- Don't do too much – it's not about how much you move, but *how* you move.
- Be aware; look around you, not at the floor.

There are lots of internet sites offering to teach people to dance, so you don't even have to leave your own home as you struggle through the first stages. Or for a more exotic scenario you could head for a belly dancing course (also available online) and wow your partner with your technique.

'Fantasy is a necessary ingredient in living.'
DR SEUSS

2

The five sexiest surprises

Here are five sizzling surprises to spring on your man. Don't try them all at once!

- After a sedate dinner (once the kids have gone to bed) tell your partner that pudding is on you. Literally. Get the ice cream and spread it all over.
- Go to dinner at your in-laws wearing no underwear. But be sure to let him know you're not wearing any just as you get out of the car. He can mull over the fact all through dinner and ravish you on your way home.

- Rent a porn movie. Nothing too drastic. We're not talking hairy men shagging horses. Watch it together with a bottle of champagne.

- Go to bed in suspenders and stockings on what is otherwise a normal weekday. Obviously you need to make sure he sees them! So saunter oh-so-casually past him to get a glass of water or turn on the alarm clock.
- Treat him to a surprise day in a spa (really). Enjoy all the facilities on offer; the sauna, Jacuzzi and pool. Just focus on yourselves and your bodies for 24 hours; what could be better than that? Once back in your room, try out some of the massage techniques you've experienced on each other.

3

Five more sexy surprises

If you've already run out of ideas then here are five more to get his imagination working overtime.

- Pounce! This will obviously only work if you're alone in the house. Pick your moment and pounce on your partner. The unexpected approach will be a huge turn on. Just make sure it's somewhere less obvious than the bedroom. Go for the bathroom, or the kitchen table. Remember that scene in *The Postman Always Rings Twice* – Jack Nicholson and Jessica Lange covered in flour and consumed with passion.

- Sex slaves – promise to be his or her sex slave for the next two hours.
- Promise him five blow jobs whenever he wants them. The generosity of this gift will touch any man. And amaze most of them. Men's most common complaint about their sex life is that they never get blow jobs from their partners.
- Check out a new position on the internet or in a book and try it out on him or her.
- Invite him to go to a sex shop with you. You don't need to buy the double headed black mamba for heaven's sake. In fact some sex shops now (Ann Summers for example) are perfectly respectable places to be seen in. And you never know what you might find.

4

Get out of bed

The chaise longue – what a piece of kit. It immediately conjures up images of raunchy 17th century sex. Take a look at the film Dangerous Liaisons if you don't know what we're talking about.

Sex on a bed is all very well, but don't ignore the potential of other pieces of furniture for creating a sexy mood and acting as great props in your fantasies. So if you want to spice things up think about how to use your home to its best potential.

Explore every room in your home for new sexy possibilities and think how a simple prop may transform a room into a sex den. Invest in a sheepskin rug for in front of your fire and suddenly you're transported to your own romantic log cabin. A dozen candles to light your bathroom will turn it into a sensual spa. The possibilities are endless.

Don't act like you've been planning it all day. Just grab the moment and don't think too deeply about it. Pounce on your partner in the bathroom for example and take things from there. Or tell him or her you've been thinking about having sex on a particular chair all day (in fact chairs are great, he sits, she straddles – think about Christine Keeler and how good she looked in *that* picture). All you need to do is use your imagination. Think laterally.

5

Three movie fantasies to recreate

Movies are great fantasy inspiration – the scenario is already set up for you and you get to emulate the sexiest people in the world.

Check out *The Fabulous Baker Boys*. Sparks fly over the piano between Michelle Pfeiffer and Jeff Bridges. The tension between the two of them crackles throughout, leading up to the stunningly sexy piano scene where they almost make love through the song. It's a great lesson in mixing work and pleasure. Watch the film and if you have a piano try it at home. Almost worth buying one for.

Next up is *Dangerous Liaisons* – more Michelle Pfeiffer and a bodice-ripping drama set in eighteenth century France. A great lesson in the dangers of immoral love as well as how to look sexy in a corset! Some of the scenes are well worth trying to recreate, such as the one where the wicked Valmont pens a letter to his victim using Uma Thurman's buttocks as a writing desk.

And finally what about *Sex, Lies and Videotape* – the title says it all. Infidelity, lust, pervy filming and sex. And a good idea for some very entertaining fun at home. Get out your video camera or just a normal stills camera if you don't have one. Make your own porn-film. Just remember to put it somewhere safe when you've finished so you don't mix it up with the one of your nephew's christening.

If regular Hollywood films aren't exciting enough go for porn if you like. It is important that you choose something that turns you on. Some people like to see every bump and grind while others prefer something more subtle, so figure out where your tastes lie and (as long as it's legal) go for it.

6

Sex on the brain

For a lot of people, especially women, sex is as much in the mind as in the more obvious erogenous zones.

For a woman to feel sexy her mind needs to be in tune with her body. And fantasy helps that enormously. Encourage your partner to help you fantasise as you are having sex. During foreplay he might whisper fantasy situations in your ear: 'Imagine we are at the opera. We are alone in the royal box. I am sitting behind you and I start caressing you, putting my hands under your dress, feeling the tops of your stockings. Everyone is watching the stage. We are trying to be as quiet as possible. I ease you off your chair and onto my lap...' You can continue the script from here.

Research has shown that short bursts of sexy thoughts throughout the day have a cumulative effect on your sex drive. Whenever you have a spare moment think about the last time you had sex, or what you plan to do with your partner that night. Fantasise. Priming your mind primes your body. It makes you want sex more – and that's very sexy.

One survey found that the beach works. Lying naked on a hot, deserted beach gets women going. Sex with an entire sports team excited some and women also like the idea of a stranger in the night who is going to take them to some seedy hotel room and pleasure them for hours. The most popular one though was the thought of being tied up and dominated.

For men the most popular fantasy is the age-old threesome (with two women). The most common scenario is having oral and genital sex at the same time. Another popular one is watching two women having sex. In fact anything to do with two women seems to work for most men.

7

Spice up your life

Time to reinvigorate yourself with something completely different.

You have already taken an important first step by buying this book. It is packed full of fantasy tips that can improve your sexiness and emotional life. Another major step is to make routine a thing of the past.

So think of ways to surprise your man. You might offer to wash his car, wearing a short skirt and stockings and suspenders. The neighbours will be eternally grateful too. Use your imagination to surprise people, including yourself!

Men are easy to please really. As long as they have food, drink, sex and are not uncomfortable they're pretty happy. Out of that list sex probably comes first so you need to come up with something that involves just that. Why not offer him one of his fantasies as a present? If that means you have to dress up in a bunny-girl outfit then so be it. You could also offer to be his sex slave for a couple of hours. The important thing is to try something you wouldn't normally do. And whatever it is, make sure he returns the favour one day soon!

8

Tie me up, tie me down 1

The first time someone ties you up is a revelation. You are no longer in control and with that comes a feeling of total abandonment.

It is a fact that most men and women love to be dominated. Not all the time, but some of the time. One of the most popular female fantasies is one that involves a man forcing himself on a woman, either by tying her up or simply holding her arms down above her head. We have all read those stories of powerful men liking a good whipping by a dominatrix. What is it about bondage that turns us on?

According to research, 14% regularly enjoy bondage (and there must be plenty more that don't admit to practising it). Men find women with whips in their hands very sexy. Maybe it's the fact a woman with a whip in her hand is unlikely to be there for anything other than a serious sex session. If it's a look you haven't tried before then you might be delighted with the effect it has on your bloke. Complete the image with a corset, stockings, high heels and suspenders. You'll have him whimpering.

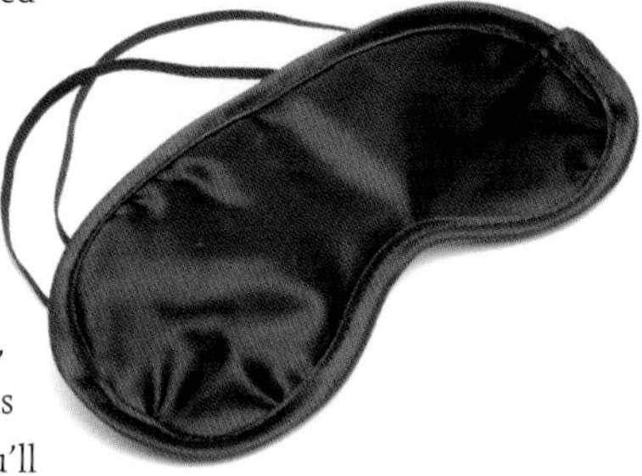

9

The cinq à sept

Take the wildness of an affair and translate it to your present relationship.

The French have managed to institutionalise infidelity. They call it the cinq à sept, the idea being that you visit your mistress on your way back home from the office in the hours between five and seven.

What is so sexy about affairs is that there is something totally enticing and tantalising about the forbidden. Those moments together are so sweet because they are (a) stolen, (b) short and (c) passionate. Combine those three factors and you have a hot situation that doesn't have a chance to burn out. There is also the danger factor in the affair situation which makes it very exciting.

Pretend to have an affair – with your partner. Plan to meet in a bar where no one will recognise you. Get that spark back into your relationship by treating each other as forbidden fruit, pretend to be working together or married to other people. Over drinks or dinner pretend you don't know each other, have never met. Invent another personality. Tell each other stories you've never previously shared. Surprise each other.

Role play can be a bit excruciating until you get used to it. Alcohol helps. As do props. Pretend you are having an affair with your doctor or that your mechanic popped round to fix a flat tyre. A white coat or a whiff of petrol will help the fantasy.

Take the 5 to 7 literally. If you meet up in a hotel room for some mad passion on your way home from work and give yourselves a time constraint you'll naturally focus on the passion and avoid the mundane.

10

Sex in strange places 1

What was the strangest place you had sex? How was it? Exciting, weird, scary?

If you think about it you'll probably find it was a mixture of all of the above. But the main thing is that it is definitely memorable. Now is the time to create a few more sexy memories.

There are some obvious places to start, quite a few of them in the comfort of your own home. The shower is one: the mixture of water and sex works brilliantly. The bath is another good place. Sofas are incredibly underrated, the possibilities are endless and there's nothing like sex on a sofa to take you back to your teenage years. Try swinging from the legendary chandelier if you happen to have one. Just make sure it's securely fastened.

Cars are great for illicit sex, even small ones, though you obviously have to be a bit more supple to avoid obstacles such as brakes, gear sticks and door handles. Another good option (assuming you're not on the hard shoulder of the M6) is sex on the warm bonnet. And, yes, the mile-high club is a bit of a cliché but it is certainly a good way to get through a long and boring flight.

11

All in the mind

Any sexual thought is sexual fantasy. And any sort of sexual thought gets the job done.

Counsellor Sarah Litvinoff says, 'Sex therapists often find that women who claim never to have been sexually interested or who have gone off sex, never think sexual thoughts. Many people narrowly define sexual fantasies as the mini-pornographic scenes you play out in your head, which might include, say, bondage or lesbian images, that are a mental turn-on, but which you wouldn't necessarily enjoy enacting for real. But it does not have to be this structured. Let your mind wander, look for the lascivious and feel the throb of sex that is lying beneath the layers of your sophisticated lifestyle.

Find stimulation in your daily routine and you'll find yourself overspilling with erotic charge, which will translate into action. You will initiate sex and respond to your partner in a different way sexually. You'll be gagging for it.

Begin to make a habit of daydreaming about sex. First thing when you wake up in the morning or last thing before you go to sleep, think a dirty thought or two. When you're commuting, let the last time you made love run through your mind. As you're queuing or waiting for your train, relive your sexual greatest hits. Count the number of people you meet in a day who actively appeal to you. Seek to get aroused by other people, but obviously don't act on it. That old chestnut about taking the energy back to stoke the home fires isn't an old chestnut for nothing.

Remember that every time sex flits across your mind it's a fantasy, and that those who fantasise most have the best sex lives. NB Like faith healing, you don't have to believe in this for it to work.

12

Paying for it 1

Slut sex can be a massive turn-on for both of you.

Both sexes can get a huge kick from acting out prostitution fantasies. This explores our attitudes to power and control (often erotically charged) and both sexes are able to relish the freedom of imagining that they're having no-holds-barred, no-strings-attached sex.

The 'client' gets the thrill of the clean transaction, of the freedom of asking for what he wants, of control, of being in charge. The 'whore' gets the visible proof that he values what she does in bed. (For the sake of clarity, we're being all traditional and assuming 'he' is the client and 'she' the whore but, of course, this fantasy begs for role reversal. The powerful female client and the stud-for-hire can be just as much of a turn-on.)

This is one that definitely works better if you've both had a couple of drinks beforehand because alcohol removes the self-consciousness from role-playing, and for this idea to really work you both need to stay in character throughout.

The Classic

Arrange to meet on a certain street corner at a certain time. Make sure there's not the slightest chance of it being mistaken for a red-light area or you might get more reality than you bargained for. She should dress as overtly sexily as she feels comfortable with in public; simply slipping off her knickers beforehand will give that added frisson. At the appointed hour, he pulls up in his car and asks whether she is available. She replies, 'For what?' Then he tells her in explicit detail. She comes back with the cost. Haggling or 'negotiating a price' can be a turn-on, and she shouldn't get in the car until the deal is done. You can now either drive back home and pretend it's her place or, if you're daring, use the car (somewhere private, of course, or again this game could get a bit too real).

13

Paying for it 2

Here's one for those of you who like your slut sex a little more glamorous.

The Pick-up

She's sitting at a hotel bar, looking sexy but demure. It helps if she adopts a slightly different look from usual – more make-up, hair slightly different, heels higher – a look that makes her feel unlike herself. She should make sure her underwear is brand new – nothing he's ever seen before. She should order a different drink from usual and adopt a different name and personality – the easier the new persona comes to her the more convincing this will be. The same applies to him: he should invent a new persona, too, and 'work it up'. He approaches her and, although there may be some preliminary

'soft soap', eventually a conversation not unlike the one above has to take place. Maintain eye contact. It's sexier. When you're done head home (or better still, take a room). Don't talk too much and stay in character when you do.

There's an easy way to add a heightened sense of reality to the fantasy of paid-for sex: she keeps the money.

14

Paying for it 3

If you really want to make a performance out of your role play then this idea should inspire you.

The Hotel Room

Book a hotel room and pay for it in advance. She arrives first and changes – a wig if she can bear it, lingerie he's never seen before, heels, different perfume, negligée if she's uncomfortable strutting around near naked. Make the mood seductive with music and candles. She should psych herself up – she's a high-class call girl and her job is to make him feel good. High-class call girls are paid a lot because they're brilliant actresses – so she should put her heart into it. At last, he knocks on the door and she lets him in. Introduce yourselves by different names. Open a bottle of champagne. He can be nervous – that's still in character. But she must be confident and tease, flirt or be sexually voracious. She should read her client and take her clues from him (he, of course, has to act out his other side – the side that frequents prostitutes). She must make it clear she's here for one reason only – to give him the best sexual experience he's ever had. What would it take?

What does he like? She should name her price and make it high. She's the ultimate indulgence. She's *expensive*. When the price has been agreed and she has the cash, lead him to the bed and get down to business. She should remember that this is her job and she's very, very good at it. If she can slip a few tricks in that he definitely won't be expecting, all the better. Maintain roles until the door closes behind him.

'You always pay for sex, but not always in cash.'
ANONYMOUS

15

Surprise for him!

Isn't it time you got in touch with your creative side?

Laura Corn, author of *101 Nights of Grrreat Sex*, has based her considerable best-selling success on one simple concept: the importance of the surprise factor. Each of her 101 suggestions depends on the fact that your partner doesn't have a clue what sexual delight you're planning. It works. Surprise your lover sexually every week for a year and you can bet your booty you won't be collecting any 'boring in bed' prizes.

A little bit of effort to surprise your lover with a new technique, seduction, outfit or behaviour reaps huge improvements. As long as it's something unexpected, the surprise can be whatever you like. It can be filthy, funny,

sweet and romantic or it can be more embarrassing than karaoke night down your local. Here are just two ideas to get you started.

- He's in the shower. Wait until it's good and steamy in there and then slip in beside him wearing your flimsiest, sheerest underwear. If there's one thing more likely to turn him on than you naked, it's wet, clinging wisps of material. (Blokes could try this, too, but it has to be silk boxers – soggy, cotton Y-fronts just don't cut it.)
- On your next date, you can keep your coat on. Well, you don't want the whole restaurant to know you're naked underneath. Just him.

16

Surprise for her!

Some of your surprises will be easy to organise. Some will take more planning.

You might spend an hour (or more) setting up a gorgeous seduction for your mate, which is a lot, fair enough, but the end result (and this is no exaggeration) will be burned into the hard drive of her memory for the rest of their life. Great sex has that sort of effect on us.

Do something slightly different *every* time you have sex. Throw in an element of surprise. Mixing it up will become second nature after a few weeks and the payoff will make it worthwhile.

Try customising some of the following suggestions to get her going:

- Buy her half a case of her favourite wine (a dozen bottles is classier, but might be too much of a demand on your imagination). Around the neck of each, place a sealed envelope containing details of where and when you're going to drink it together. These are IOUs of pleasure. Let your imagination run riot.
- One night when you're getting amorous in a lovey-dovey sort of way, suddenly flip personality – change the whole atmosphere. From Dr Jekyll to Mr Hyde. Stop smiling. Get mean. Overcome her. Tie her wrists to the headboard and blindfold her. Now you can do whatever you like, but if you want to give her a night to remember (and especially if she's still really pissed off with you), go down on her until she stops cursing and starts begging.
- Spend an hour or so pleasuring her sensually, such as oral sex, washing her hair, painting her toenails, applying body lotion to every inch of her skin or holding her and stroking her hair until she falls asleep. Don't allow her to do a thing for you in return.

17

Two clichéd (and-that's-because-they-work) fantasy role plays

Before you know it, you'll be down the local fancy-dress shop for your Robin Hood or nun's outfit.

Some people find costumes liberating and that they help them get into character. Some people find them inhibiting, not to say ridiculous. But don't give up too early on them because they can help.

Doctor and nurse

It's the end of another gruelling day on the wards. The nurse (either one of you) is looking exhausted. The doctor calls the nurse over and says, 'You're looking tired. Could you do with a complete examination?' The doctor gets the examination table ready and asks the nurse to lie down on it. A complete medical later and the diagnosis is 'nervous tension'. However, the doctor is conducting a scientific study into this condition, with some controversial treatment options. If the nurse is willing to take part in some medical experimentation and give feedback on how well the cure works, the doctor will demonstrate the technique...

Master and slave

One of you is the cruel master (or mistress); one is the gorgeous slave. The master is deciding whether to buy or not, which involves a thorough examination. The slave is wrapped in layers of clothes and drapes but is slowly stripped (or ordered to strip) so the master can confirm that the slave is in good physical condition – and that means that every bit of them is in good physical condition. Then, of course, the slave's ability to follow orders and please the master will have to be tested...

Crack open a bottle (or two). As with all fantasy games, alcohol helps loosen you up. A lot.

18

Another clichéd (and brilliant) fantasy role play

Pick a night to play out your fantasy, although sometimes it's best just to go for it spontaneously as it helps you to feel less self-conscious.

Even if the first time is a disaster and lasts about two minutes before you start laughing, at least you've made a start. You won't have to expend any money on special outfits unless you want to, as you can improvise with dressing up and

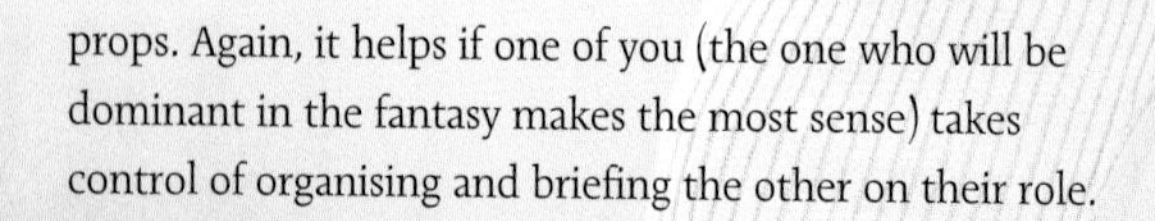

props. Again, it helps if one of you (the one who will be dominant in the fantasy makes the most sense) takes control of organising and briefing the other on their role.

Boss and interviewee

The interviewee comes to the office after hours to be interviewed for their dream job. The interview starts normally: the interviewee is anxious to please and the interviewer is gracious. However, when they start discussing terms of employment, some of the terms are quite unusual. Late-night working? Threesomes with the head of personnel and the boss? Finally, there is an initiative test – how well the interviewee performs determines whether they get the job...

19

Even more clichéd (and brilliant) fantasy role plays

Acting out fantasies takes a bit of practice, but can certainly brighten up a boring Saturday night.

First get into bed and talk dirty to one another. Read from some mildly pornographic books (or filthy pornographic books, if you like). Share some situations that turn you on mentally. Talk through the sorts of things you'd like to say or do.

Handyman and housewife

He arrives ready for work, but she insists he has a cup of tea and a chat. While she's showing him the problem 'with her pipes', she gets into such a position that he can't help noticing she's not wearing any underwear...

Naughty maid and 'master of the house'

She's supposed to be cleaning the house when the 'master' comes home and discovers her 'pleasuring' herself instead. He's furious and threatens her with dismissal. She is beside herself. She'll lose her job. She has to think of something quick that will persuade him that sacking her is a bad idea...

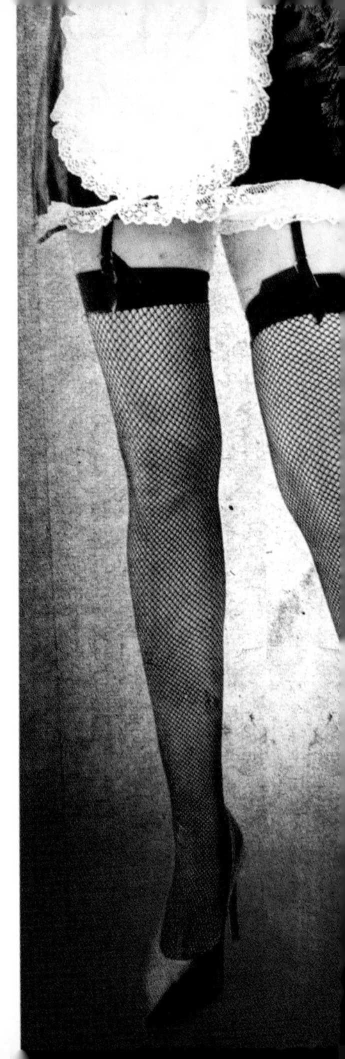

20

Pain games

In forgoing all control, there's a whole heap of freedom.

What people love about hard-core health spas – the ones where you get timetables and set menus involving lots of lentils – is that you don't have to think. You just do what you're told. That's what the submissive partner gets in B&D games.

The pain you experience in these sorts of games isn't pain like when you catch your finger in the door. When pain is anticipated, it raises your heart rate and releases the feel-good hormones endorphins – just what happens during exercise. One effect of this is that you can experience heightened sexual pleasure and sensation. When things get painful, try deep steady breathing, which makes sexual sensations even stronger.

- Spanking. Always warm up the spankee's buttocks beforehand with some gentle slaps and then build up in a rhythmic way with gaps between strokes. The back of a hairbrush or a table tennis bat make good alternatives if your hand is getting sore. As a general rule, never hit any part of the body that is hard. In fact, don't hit anything but the buttocks unless you know what you're doing. After administering a whupping and when the skin is still pink and tingly, run your fingers gently over their skin. This will feel exquisite.
- Nipple clamps. Experiment first with nipping close to orgasm to see if it's you or your partner's thang. Those who like this *really* like it.

We're assuming that when we're not dressing up as naughty schoolgirls and irate headmasters we're all sensible adults and don't need it spelt out that this is potentially dangerous stuff. When playing with power games that involve humiliation and control there's always the chance you'll hurt another person, and not just physically. You should both agree on a word beforehand that immediately signals 'game's over, time for lots of cuddling and reassurance'.

21

Power games

For the dominant partner – what's not to love? They get to do exactly what they want, exactly the way they like it.

This is perfect for anal compulsives, who most of the time can't get the rest of us to do it their way. On our knees, on our back, tied up, tied down or licking the heel of your shoes for twenty minutes. It's your call.

It goes without saying that all of this goes down well with a bit of role-play. Modify some of the following scenarios, or make up your own. It's your night to shine. Or to be hogtied and locked in a cupboard, if that's what lights your candle.

- Tying up. Play with exposure (generally, the wider the limbs are spread, the more you feel like you're open to the public – some people like that). Restraints on all four limbs are great for people who find it hard to come because of performance pressure to 'get there'. Restraint puts you totally at the mercy of your partner. You are in their power. They have responsibility. You can relax. Whoosh. Was that an orgasm?
- Gags. This is more a mind thing than anything else. It looks great and it makes you feel really helpless – loads of opportunity to flail your head from side to side in best teen-slasher movie style. Tongue over the gag, please. Blindfolds work, too. The more senses you cut off – sight, speech, hearing – the more you're forced to concentrate on what you're feeling.

And remember: no tying up for more than half an hour unless you're an expert boy scout; never leave a tied up person alone without checking on them; no whips near the eyes.

22

Danger (soft core)

Danger is the fastest-acting aphrodisiac.

In a famous experiment, an attractive scientist interviewed two groups of men. The first group had a standard interview. The second were interviewed after they'd crossed a particularly hairy rope bridge. By the time they were interviewed, their palms were sweaty and their hearts beating fast. This group of men found the same interviewer significantly more alluring. The danger had heightened their sexual response.

No one's suggesting that you set yourself up for anything life threatening, but sharing adventures together will do the job – especially physical adventures. Adventures count as anything that gets your adrenaline flowing. It needn't necessarily be dangerous. You're simply seeking a shared experience that gets both of your hearts thumping.

Five (soft core) ideas:

- Go to Alton Towers, Disneyland or anywhere with fast, high rides.
- Dare each other.
- Have sex where you might just be seen.
- Stay the night somewhere reputedly haunted, but definitely creepy.
- Shop at a sex shop together.

That old chestnut of making a list of six escapades to try and then letting a dice decide which you'll undergo together brings a delicious thrill of Russian roulette to the proceedings.

If it all seems a bit out-doorsy for your partner try doing things differently, possibly pushing him out of his comfort zone a little. For example, suggest that you meet at the Prada in Madrid on a particular Saturday next month. You have to get there alone. You're not allowed to confer in any way. Travel separately and check-in to separate hotels. Meet. It's not exactly dangerous but you'll have each had separate experiences, met different people and had to think outside the box – a first step to living more exciting lives.

23

Danger (hard core)

Danger makes life seem more intense and heightens sexual desire along with everything else.

In an experiment, male volunteers were each assigned an attractive female assistant. They were told the experiment was investigating electric shock treatments. Some men were told they were in the control group so they wouldn't be receiving shocks. The rest were told they were going to receive painful jolts of electricity. Then they were asked how attracted they felt to their research partner. The ones who were nervously awaiting the shocks found the same women significantly more attractive than the control group.

As well as making life seem more intense danger provides that old old 'caveman' thing. Share danger together and the bloke gets the chance to look after the female, and she gets to feel all fragile and protected even if she's a cut-throat investment banker who fries balls before breakfast in real life. If you're feeling adventurous then here are four hard-core ideas:

- Have sex when other people could definitely see you. (Be subtle – you don't want to frighten the horses or get arrested.)
- Go white-water rafting, bungee jumping or parachute jumping.
- Take your clothes off at midnight at the end of your street.
- Go to amateur night at your local comedy club together. Stand up and be funny.

24

Dirty little secrets 1

The plan here is to create the sex equivalent of the perfect holiday.

You know something about your partner that no one else knows. OK, you two have secrets already – you know hundreds of things about your partner that no one else knows. But, by sharing sexual secrets, you become even closer. That's because you underline the uniqueness of your relationship – *no one else* but you two knows these secrets. And, of course, creating the secrets is the real fun.

A good example of a sexual secret is to shave off each other's pubic hair. This is still mildly shocking, though God knows why with the ubiquity of the Brazilian wax. Besides the frisson of naughtiness, there's a practical reason to try shaving. Being hairless increases sensation, especially during oral sex. Plus, in a crowded room, you'll be the only one who knows why they're squirming about so much in their seat when the hair starts to regrow. But despite the itch, it's well worth trying at least once because it really redefines the meaning of 'intimacy'. First trim with small nail scissors (you see why this is so intimate), then bathe and then lather up with hair conditioner. Next, apply liberal amounts of shaving gel, and use disposable razors to carefully shave off the hair. Use your hand to smooth down areas like the labia to get a good line. Women, ask your man for advice – they know more about this than you do. You could experiment with heart shapes or trimming initials if you don't want to go the whole way. Apply hypoallergenic lotion afterwards to soothe it all down, which also helps when the hair's growing back. Besides the risqué, using daily everyday objects to filthy effect is another good ruse. For instance, use lipstick to draw around your penis, nipples or labia. Have your partner lick and suck it off. That takes a lot of suction and you'll never hear the word 'lipstick' together again without looking at each other knowingly.

25

Wait. We said wait! (For her)

Delay orgasm and you'll know the true meaning of 'climb every mountain'.

A woman's biggest fear is that with the winning line in sight, he changes his stroke, everything goes pear-shaped and she doesn't make it.

So, when a woman feels herself on the edge of an orgasm she'll rush her way there. It's hard-earned and she wants it now. But here's another way for her to do it. On the point of orgasm, she could slow down, relax, breathe deeply, wait a moment or so and then let the tension build again.

Experiment with this (either with your partner or while masturbating) to discover how long you have to stop–start, stop–start to get the most explosive orgasms. When you do allow yourself to come, clenching buttocks and inner thighs, deep breathing and pressing down just above your pubic bone all increase blood flow, which keeps the sensation going.

Theoretically, if a woman can come once, she can come multiple times. It's commonly believed that straight after a woman has come, she can't bear to have her clitoris touched. Sometimes true, but not always. Experiment with different techniques during masturbation. Swap to a different hand motion after you've come, or if you're using a vibrator try a different hot spot. Keep stimulation constant, but varied. Once you have the hang of that, masturbate to orgasm and stop masturbating completely after the first orgasm. Wait thirty seconds and then apply the same stimulation to the clitoris again. Shorten the waiting period until you can keep the stimulation constant without it being uncomfortable, and experience orgasm after orgasm rolling over you.

26

Wait. We said wait! (For him)

How to have more, longer and better orgasms.

Advocates of all ways Eastern recommend 'injaculation', a way that a man can experience multiple orgasms by 'coming' without ejaculation. This means he can go again right away, experience multiple bliss and, of course, keep going longer.

How to do it? Business as usual until just before the 'point of no return'. Then swiftly, either you or your partner applies circular (quite heavy) pressure to your perineum, the space midway between your anus and the root of your penis. This causes pressure on the urethra and will stop you ejaculating, although you should still experience a deeply pleasurable, not to say mind-boggling, sensation. And you should still be hard – ready to play again should the mood take you. And it will, of course.

Play a game where you oil each other and try to give your mate an orgasm with a different part of your body from usual. You can also go for the blended orgasm. This means applying stimulation at different pleasure points so excitement mounts. He can stimulate her G-spot, her clitoris and her perineum one after another in rotation. She can stimulate the head of his penis, the shaft and the prostate in rotation. This takes time, but should result in a long delayed and sweeter blend of intense pleasure and melting ecstasy when you come.

'The golden rule of kink: only play with people who play nice. 'Cause the ex who caught you cheating and now has you cuffed and blindfolded ain't comin' back.'

EM and LO

27

Give yourself a real eye-opener

Explore voyeurism and exhibitionism and bring a completely new verboten edge to your sex life.

The following fantasy role-play depends on our love of looking and our love of being watched. Use it as a starting point to begin exploring your own voyeuristic or exhibitionistic fantasies – nearly all of us are turned on by one, and usually both. If you'd like to strip, but are too shy, then the 'Peeping Tom' fantasy in idea 28 is a good place to start. You can start dropping clothes without feeling self-conscious, as (ostensibly) you're not doing it for an audience.

Imagine...

Your partner comes home to find the house lit by candles. You lead them to the bathroom where there is a scented bath waiting. You undress, blindfold and wash them. You don't let them do anything for themselves. Then you lead them to the bedroom, also lit only by candles, where there's a huge mirror propped to give a great reflection of the bed or, if that's not possible, the floor covered in cushions and quilts. Remove the blindfold and then make love, staring at yourselves in the mirror, holding your lover's gaze. Try half closing your eyes so that you can fantasise that it isn't you, but another couple writhing inches away from you – accomplices at an orgy. Go one step further and imagine that the couple in the mirror are another couple that you're observing – to help the illusion, disguise yourselves by wearing corsets, wigs, a new pair of heels, etc.

28

Another real eye-opener

Here's another fantasy role play based on exhibitionism and voyeurism.

Imagine...

In the morning, you give your partner explicit written instructions of what you want them to do and at what hour you want them to start. At ten minutes before the appointed hour, you go to your bedroom, move clothes out of your wardrobe into the spare room, place a chair in the wardrobe and sit inside it with the door open a crack so you can see the bed.

Your partner arrives in the bedroom. He or she follows the instructions you gave them earlier. They slowly begin to get

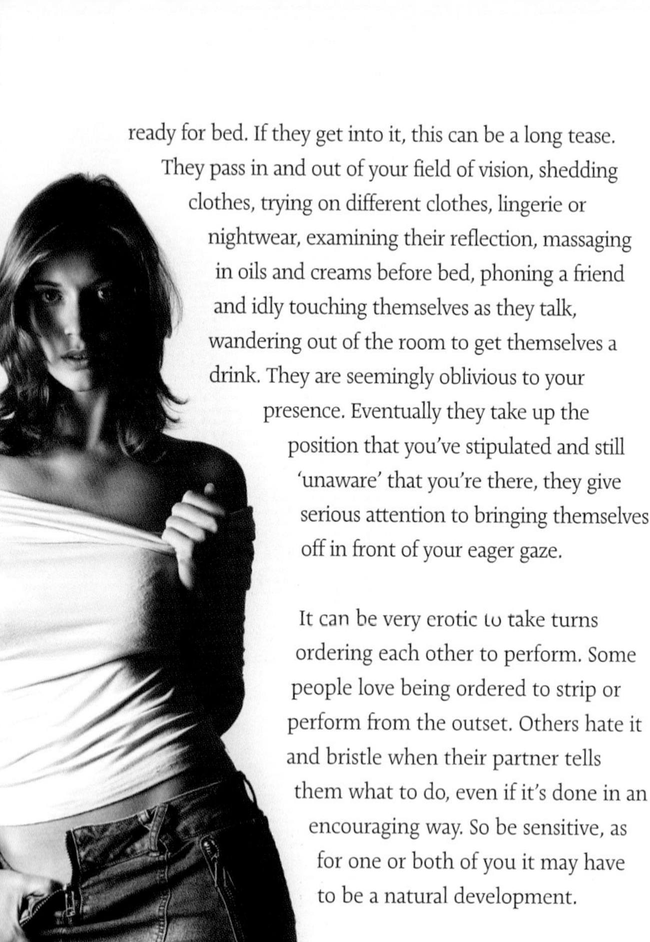

ready for bed. If they get into it, this can be a long tease. They pass in and out of your field of vision, shedding clothes, trying on different clothes, lingerie or nightwear, examining their reflection, massaging in oils and creams before bed, phoning a friend and idly touching themselves as they talk, wandering out of the room to get themselves a drink. They are seemingly oblivious to your presence. Eventually they take up the position that you've stipulated and still 'unaware' that you're there, they give serious attention to bringing themselves off in front of your eager gaze.

It can be very erotic to take turns ordering each other to perform. Some people love being ordered to strip or perform from the outset. Others hate it and bristle when their partner tells them what to do, even if it's done in an encouraging way. So be sensitive, as for one or both of you it may have to be a natural development.

29

Try another eye-opening fantasy

Welcome to our live bed show...

Imagine...

You are the stars of a live porn show. You've a clearly defined stage area (either your bed or a rug on your living room floor, brightly lit with spotlights). You both dress and prepare yourselves in your 'dressing room'. You can hear the pounding music in the background that you'll perform to and (imagine) the applause and excitement emanating from the audience. You take up position on your stage and begin to strip each other.

Remember, everyone in the club has to see every detail and every act is exaggerated to give a maximum eyeful to the people standing, craning at the back. Massage oil into each other's bodies. When you start to have sex, remember this – it's a show. Everything has to be seen. Your audience loves it, and you can feel the tense silence as they watch you strip and the growing excitement as the sex becomes more explicit, more frenzied. You two get more excited, louder, more vocal, urging each other on verbally. When he comes, it should be over her body – the so-called 'money shot' beloved of porn films.

If this sounds a bit complicated try something less elaborate. Park your car in a remote spot and play at being teenagers again. Taking risks in public will make you feel far more daring than when you genuinely were a teenager. You can still do it somewhere where you could be overlooked without taking much of a risk of it actually happening. Just thinking that you're being watched is a great turn-on.

30

Top fantasy destination

You don't necessarily need to leave the house to find great new sexual locations.

Doing it differently is part of the foundations for constantly exciting sex. Classic or clichéd, these love scenes can really get you going. Here's one for starters.

Working late at the office (your kitchen)

One of you is the boss. The boss has very high standards and expects a great deal from the assistant, who is working late one night (at your kitchen table posing as a desk), bent over their work with only a desk lamp for illumination. Suddenly, the boss strides in and throws a sheaf of papers at the hapless assistant's head and lets loose with a stream of invective along the lines of, 'This is rubbish. If you want to keep your job, you're going to have to be punished until you do it better.' The hapless assistant is tied up to a chair and stripped, while the boss begins to undress and hisses, 'You'd like to touch me, but you're so incompetent you wouldn't know what to do with it.' The boss then proceeds to show the assistant how it should be done, ordering the assistant to help make amends for past mistakes.

Plan your fantasy trip carefully. Take time to run through the scenario in your mind and write your own script (mentally). Unless you're both brilliant at improvisation and have a bit of a competitive streak, it will typically take two or three fantasy destinations for you to get a grip on it.

'I say to men, "OK, pretend you're a burglar and you break in and throw me down on the bed and make me suck your cock." And they're horrified. "No, no, it would degrade you." Exactly. Degrade me when I ask you to.'
LISA PALAC

31

Two more favourite fantasy destinations

If you enjoyed 'working late at the office', try these.

The alpine lodge in a blizzard (your living room)

It's winter. Deep winter. You are two climbers who've had to take shelter in a remote log cabin, cut off from the rest of the human race and locked fast by a blizzard. You've no electricity, little food but luckily lots of brandy. You spread a blanket in front of the log fire, light a couple of candles and sip at your brandy. Outside the wind is howling. Your fellow climber is looking more attractive by the minute. Soon it seems a very good idea to get under the blanket (or better still, into a very cosy sleeping bag) and huddle together for warmth...

The sauna (your bathroom)

It's very hot and steamy (thanks to your shower being on full). So steamy that at first you don't see that someone else is sharing the sauna with you. Then you notice a figure sitting close by wrapped in a white towel. You smile uncertainly then shut your eyes and relax, letting the steam overwhelm you. You open your eyes. Your companion is staring at you. Their towel falls open. Everyone is supposed to wear swimsuits but you never do, and they obviously don't either. You're embarrassed. Should you point out that their towel has slipped or let your own slip a little too...?

32

Shivering with anticipation (for her)

Here's how to charge yourself up into an erotic good mood.

Try to put yourself on the psychiatrist's couch and think about what situations are erotic for you. If you visualise yourself having a wonderful sexual experience, right down to the expression on your face and the perspiration dripping as you climax, it's much more likely to happen.

Another trick is to devote a little time to just thinking sexy thoughts: for instance, giving yourself a chance to daydream, browse erotica and the freedom to respond to sexual imagery. Betty Dodson suggests we tap into aural pleasure because we've been conditioned to climax and have sex silently. Try recording an orgasm with a tape recorder and playing it back; you'll probably find it's more subdued than you realise. Just practising coming in a louder, sexier way can supercharge your sex life.

Get into the habit of writing down your dreams. When you go to sleep, think erotic thoughts and hopefully you'll have raunchy dreams all night – which will mean you'll wake up feeling wet and ready for a bit of love. The more you can train yourself to think sexy at odd times, like when you're waiting in a supermarket queue, the faster you'll be able to perform when it really counts.

'Made a hell of a discovery the other night. Eyelashes on the clit...can blink her off in no time.'

DAN JENKINS

33

Mind games

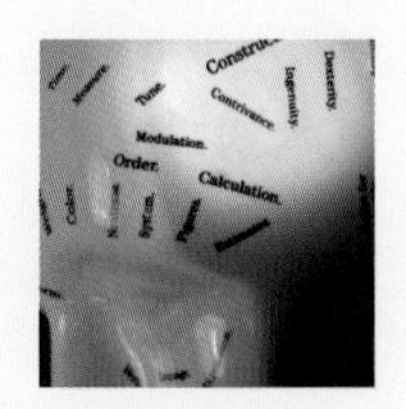

Building up an elaborate fantasy life is fun, creative and free, plus you get to know more about the hidden depths of each other's psyche!

The delicious thing about head play is that you can talk over the details first at length and use this to get each other off. You might want to invest in some props to make it more authentic. For women, a wig and certain types of shoes and/or underwear are very effective, and it's a great excuse to play around with make-up, temporary tattoos and accessories. Just like making a film, you come up with a script, work out the characters, sets and costumes, and then set it up so it's ready to roll.

Constructing an elaborate fantasy that you can both get into is ideal for taking a short cut to getting in the mood: he plays a certain music track or says the magic word and – boom – you're horny! This works if you indulge in it occasionally, so don't be afraid to act out. You can be whoever you want to be!

Remember your dolls' tea set and the fun you had with it? Get your partner to secretly set up lots of things in small dishes that you can use erotically such as ice, warm water, egg white (a natural lubricant), ice cream, honey, pieces of fruit, rose petals, sex toys. Your partner blindfolds you and gets you to investigate what's waiting inside each dish and helps you to make the most of it...

34

Porn star protocol 1

Porn star Stormy Daniels gives us the low-down on her job, her love life and her top sex tips.

'Luckily, I get to pick the people that I work with so I'm almost always looking forward to it,' she says. She'll talk to the actors beforehand and agree on what kind of sex they'll get into: 'Every time I do a scene with someone I've already worked with, it's easier because you learn with that person, just like in your personal life.' Talk to your partner first about positions you're keen to try and come up with a script you can play with. Stormy admits her day job didn't teach her everything; a good relationship helped her to find another sexual dimension: 'It wasn't until I was with the person I'm with now that I could have a G-spot orgasm and that's because I was looking in the wrong place!' Every sexual partner can teach you something different, so make more of an effort to reach new sexual highs.

She doesn't pre-lubricate herself beforehand and says to get herself psyched up she'll go and watch scenes being filmed: 'It's kind of like watching real porn!' It especially helps her get in the mood 'if there's someone who's really having a good time'. The hair and make-up preparation also helps too. 'It's the same with people in their personal lives; you might not really feel like having sex so much but you go and take a shower and shave your legs and then you're more open to the idea.' Stormy suggests that if you feel beautiful before you have sex, you're more likely to enjoy yourself.

"When pornography sneezes, pop culture catches cold.'

IRVINE WELSH

35

Porn star protocol 2

More porn star tips from Stormy Daniels.

Stormy recommends fantasy and experimentation. 'The first time I had sex in front of a mirror was just amazing because I could see something to help me visualise. To this day this memory is still something I think about when I'm having sex on camera and need to get in the mood.' Find your own personal 'trigger' fantasy to help get you there.

Her advice to women looking to be a bit more orgasmic is 'Have sex with yourselves to find out what you like. Speak up and say what you want and experiment in bed. If women stop having sex, they stop craving it. But once you get started, the more sex you have, the more you want it.'

Try preparing yourself to be 'on call' like a porn star and wait in a carefully appointed dressing room. Get your partner to pop his head in every now and then and bring you drinks... you'll be fresh and looking gorgeous, and perhaps waiting for your partner until he says 'they' are ready for you will heighten your anticipation.

Stormy Daniels says, 'The best position for orgasm for most women is woman on top. If your partner's having sex with you, obviously he likes you, otherwise his penis wouldn't be hard, right? So don't be shy. Pornography is a great way to break the ice. You've got to experiment. For the longest time I didn't even like oral sex; for me it was a waste of time. Not to give it, but to get it. I had a partner that just loved doing it and after a while I learned to enjoy it too.'

36

Indecent proposal

Women think about sex at least four and a half times a day. The trick is to hold on to some of these fleeting images so you can make use of them.

Keep a dream/mood diary, and note down things and people that arouse a flicker of sexual interest – find out what turns you on.

Some women find their wildest thoughts are actually quite mundane. Don't worry if your fantasy isn't exotic, as the most common one is sex with a current or past lover. To get more acquainted with your secret fantasies, browse books, websites and erotic films for inspiration. Try to spend some time in the week on your own, safe behind a locked door. Some find sanctuary in the bathroom, where they can sip a glass of wine as they soak in the bath and let their mind wander. Let your thoughts take you wherever they want to go, and resist the urge to self-censor.

To delve deeper into his sexual psyche, get your partner to write his secret fantasies on your back with a lip liner pencil. You won't be able to see them unless you look in a mirror (and then you have to be able to read backwards) so his secret is safe unless he can trust you enough to reveal all. If you only get part of the way in one session, have a bath and get him to wash it all off.

But who can we trust to tell us what good sex is? Should we ask people who have a lot of sexual experience, or people who have a lot of research experience?'

KATH ALBURY

37

Beyond the beyond

The road to excess leads to the palace of wisdom. Tips for the sexually adventurous (not for the faint-hearted).

For advanced play you need new techniques. For example, instead of just penetration, you might want to experiment with fisting which is popular among lesbians.

Start by lubricating with a water-based lube and playing around with one finger, adding others one at a time. You have to be incredibly horny to be able to enjoy this. Using lots of stimulation and lube, get him to play with you and slowly add more fingers. See how far you can go. If he can insert four fingers, you're nearly there and it's just a question of him squashing his fingers together and twisting his hand to go further in. If it becomes uncomfortable, take some of the fingers out or stop altogether. A diagonal route is the best way to get the whole hand in.

Some women describe being fisted as the ultimate orgasm and when this happens, your muscles might clench so much they push his hand out. He has to go with the flow, but must never take his hand out quickly – it can take as long to get out as it took to get in, so this is not an activity to do in the five minutes before bedtime. If the vaginal opening forms what Califia describes as a 'vacuum seal' around his wrist, get him to insert a finger to break 'the seal'.

'The real fountain of youth is to have a dirty mind.'
JERRY HALL

38

DIY porn 1

You need a lot of trust to photograph/video each other nude doing rude things, but it can build intimacy, spice up your love life and give you a few visual tips.

Begin by spending time just looking at yourself naked in front of a full length mirror. Rub body lotion or massage oil all over to give yourself a sexy sheen and practise a few poses. Go on, push out your breasts and make your back taller, pulling in your tummy. Look around from the back, sit on a chair in the famous Christine Keeler pose, try anything you like and see how it feels.

Perhaps you'll feel more comfortable photographing yourself in private first. This exercise is a great excuse to buy something sexy, and remember the easiest way to make a naked body look better is to get an even tan and to regularly moisturise all over, so do the preparation work. You can set up a video camera and leave it running whilst you practise walking, undressing, posing or even masturbating. Play it back to yourself later and note how you moved and how any clothes you wore suited you. This is a great opportunity to parade around in those sexy items lurking at the back of the drawer. You could also use the photo function on your mobile phone to snap all kinds of strange positions down there, or set up a regular camera to go off at timed intervals. You'll probably find you look totally different to how you imagined: edit the film or photos, keeping the ones that are the most flattering.

39

DIY porn 2

If you want to immortalise each other together, lay down some ground rules first.

In an online article Rodney Chester warns, 'Making a porn video is just one step. What to do with it is another problem.' It could be that one of you keeps it in a safe place, or that you don masks for the filming, or only shoot non-identifiable body parts. We all know from the scandals around the Pamela Anderson, Rob Lowe and Paris Hilton tapes what happens when home-made porn leaks out.

Now you're ready to experiment. Perhaps you're choreographing everything around a narrative – like a sexy nurse and a sick patient. Take the chance to flesh out your fantasies. Later you can analyse your foreplay strategies and put a voice to the images, telling your lover what things turned you on the most. It's a chance to learn something and develop trust, and it might turn you on: it's really the perfect rainy day activity!

If you're anxious about having photos/videos hanging around, get your lover to draw you in the nude like they do in art class. Of course, he can dictate any poses he thinks fit, and they'll probably be far raunchier than the standard poses students work with.

40

Sex as sport (for her)

These days casual sex is an exciting alternative to traditional relationships. It can be an emotional minefield, though, so here's how to have the spark without getting burned.

One of the bonuses about deciding to go ahead with the chase for casual sex is that you don't know when it's going to happen. That means lots of anticipatory pleasure, soaking in luxurious baths, attending to matters of depilation and wearing knock 'em dead underwear. Just thinking about the possibility gives you a boost and any extra effort you've made will increase your confidence.

Obvious meeting places for casual sex are nightclubs, pubs and concerts, but really any social gathering offers opportunities, if you're not too shy to look for them. The advantage of seeking out a casual partner is that you can discount a lot of the attributes you'd look for in a long-term partner, and can go for physical attractiveness and sex appeal over a good sense of humour.

Don't turn cold as soon as you've come, but don't expect roses either. Discretion is everything. If you've made it clear there's no commitment, don't be afraid to be affectionate, or enjoy multiple orgasms. It's meant to be fun!

'I used to be Snow White...but I drifted.'
MAE WEST

41

The pleasure of pain

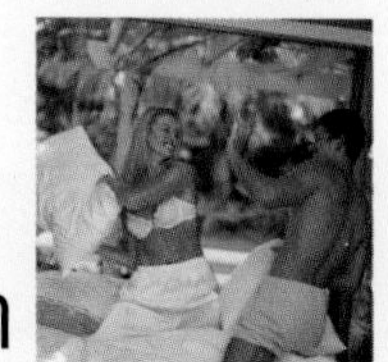

Images of kink are everywhere. Most of the time they are used to shock in advertising, but experimenting along the edges of your 'shadow selves' can lead to mind-opening experiences.

Things to try include tying someone up (bondage), tickling (with hand or feather), stroking, spanking, caning and whipping. If you want to try being submissive without all the fancy gear, you can try meting out 'school' type punishments. An easy one is making someone stand next to a wall keeping a coin in place with their nose. Bondage adds an element of fantasy (it's one of the most common ones for both men and women). Be wary about using makeshift household items like silk scarves; they are actually like wire in the wrong hands. Always pad areas that you want to bind first (handcuffs should also be padded). If in doubt, raid the kitchen for cling film and mummify your victim (don't cover the face and don't leave it on for more than an hour, though); you could try a little light spanking over the wrapping.

'My ultimate fantasy is to entice a man to my bedroom, put a gun to his head and say "make babies or die".'
RUBY WAX

42

More pleasure of pain

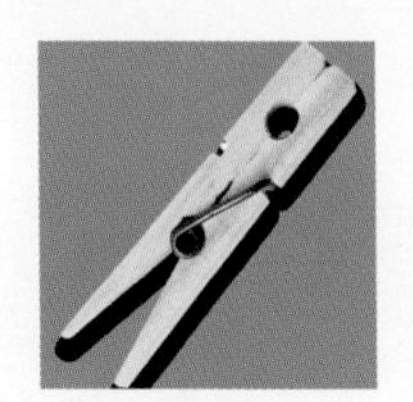

Adding a little pain to the proceedings is stimulating for some because it releases endorphins – the same feel-good chemicals we get when we exercise.

Too much pain is a turn-off, and everyone has a different pain threshold. Always remember to warm up each part of the body first: before moving on to harder strokes, you could start with stroking, move on to tickling and progress to hand

spanking then possibly using a different implement. Don't forget that faster strokes feel harder simply because the person experiencing it has less time to catch their breath. So take it slowly and experiment.

Even if you don't have any specific fetishes or S and M fantasies, most people will find it interesting to try both 'top' and 'bottom' roles. Most newbies will try being a bottom first, and in the 'scene' bottoms outnumber tops by ten to one! Although it might seem appealing to be dominant, in actual fact they are doing all the work... They are not doing whatever they want to someone, but working to a pre-agreed 'script' that should be mutually fulfilling. In addition, who is penetrated is not determined by the role they are playing. The submissive partner may be 'made' to use their mouth/penis on the other, and the dominant partner could accept or initiate sexual activity. The whole point is that it's a game where you invent your own rules. Break free from conventional constraints and find out what really turns you on!

The next time you are in the middle of foreplay, ask your partner to put their hands behind their head and close their eyes whilst you tickle them with something soft and silky. At any time they can open their eyes or release their hands, so there's no pressure. If this works, you can progress on to more exciting things...

TELEPHONE
TELEPHONE
PULL

43

Sex in strange places 2

Don't forget that if you want incredible sex you need to keep that edge. Dare to be different.

Sex in unexpected places is sexy partly because it is unexpected, but also because it is something new and exciting. Lifts are incredibly sexy places. It must be something to do with being enclosed in a small space with someone. In a lift you run the risk of being caught which only adds to the excitement. There is something extremely erotic about getting into a lift with someone you have fancied from afar for ages and imagining what you would do to him if that dweeb from accounts would only get out and leave the two of you alone together...

Done the car, the cinema and behind the filing cabinet at work? Short of new ideas? Try some of these (be sensible though, remember having sex in public places is illegal):

- A private box at the opera
- A phone box (better be quick – easy-access underwear will help)
- Your garden (put a tent up if the neighbours' twitching curtains bother you)
- The public library (not recommended for loud and energetic climaxes!)
- A hospital (better than flowers and what do you think those screens are for?)
- A rooftop (if you can get to the top of your apartment or office block)
- On the train.

Take the sex in strange places challenge – promise each other to have sex in a strange place once a week for the next two months. That's eight weird locations. Enough to have your imagination working overtime.

44

Sex in water (solo)

There's nothing quite like a bit of splashing and thrashing around in water, especially if it's combined with a bit of aqua erotica!

All your favourite sex toys come in waterproof versions, and the versatility of water makes it the ideal medium for adding the X factor to your sex life. These days, there are loads of waterproof sex toys that help you to get off discreetly. For instance, you could insert Fun Factory pleasure balls and then go for a swim in your local pool or sit in a spa. There's also the Wireless Waterproof Vibrating Panty with a wireless waterproof micro-orb that fits into the pants. Wear a swimsuit over it and nobody will notice.

Alternatively, there are plenty of bath and shower accessories that can be put to good use. Almost every type of sex toy imaginable comes in a waterproof version and you can get dildo accessories to stick on the shower door or side of the bath. Some toys look perfectly innocuous: for instance, there's a Sponge vibrator that gets you clean as well, and a Ducky vibrator that gets going when you give the little fellow a squeeze.

45

Sex in water (together)

Water is the most essential element of life, so it's not surprising we feel revitalised when we're splashing around in it.

Our bodies feel lighter immersed in it (the water takes some of the weight) and the sensation of water on our bodies kick-starts our blood circulation. In addition, during water play we're probably going to be scantily clad, and doing some invigorating form of exercise. To top it off, hopefully our bodies will be being given a dose of vitamin D from the sun: all the raw ingredients for feeling raunchy and playful. It's not surprising that sex on a summer holiday seems the best we have all year.

Pool accessories like floats, inflatable chairs and toys are all great for horsing around with. Use the opportunity to throw yourself at each other and play games on inflatable shapes. If you're in a romantic mood, use floats to support your partner's head and/or lower torso. Get your partner to close their eyes and gently wade through the water until their body is completely relaxed. If you have privacy, you can move up to genital foreplay, or use an underwater clit massager. If you don't have these options, use the water to de-stress and warm each other up before you move on to dry land, and to the real thing. If you're on a secluded lake, there's also fun stuff like an inflatable trampoline that's great for bouncy, gyrating sex. It's best to wear a life jacket just in case, and you could even go for it whilst floating in life jackets. Water sports like snorkelling are great in themselves, so it's an extra bonus if your partner massages you erotically as you're swimming along. Again, take care of safety and incorporate floats if you're in deeper water. And remember that in most places genital fondling and sex in public places is illegal!

46

Play some games

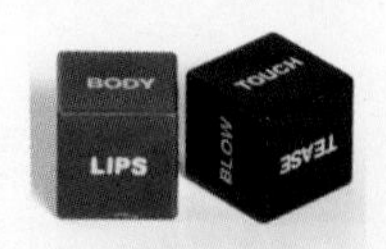

Remember the gold-covered women in Goldfinger? Here's how to paint and play with each other to your heart's content. It's silly but it works wonders.

Being playful in the bedroom can be erotically very powerful. For instance, you could play Twister naked, or stage a food fight: anything to get you having fun together. You can try strip poker or spin the bottle. A game like Nookii is designed specifically for couples and helps to initiate foreplay and

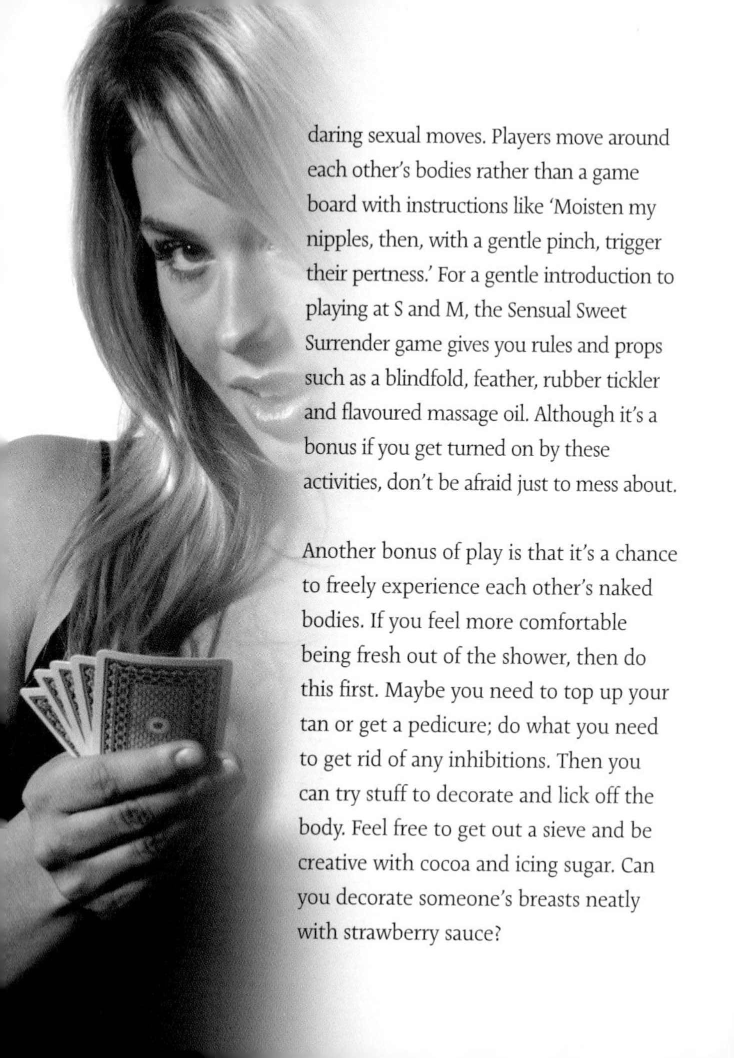

daring sexual moves. Players move around each other's bodies rather than a game board with instructions like 'Moisten my nipples, then, with a gentle pinch, trigger their pertness.' For a gentle introduction to playing at S and M, the Sensual Sweet Surrender game gives you rules and props such as a blindfold, feather, rubber tickler and flavoured massage oil. Although it's a bonus if you get turned on by these activities, don't be afraid just to mess about.

Another bonus of play is that it's a chance to freely experience each other's naked bodies. If you feel more comfortable being fresh out of the shower, then do this first. Maybe you need to top up your tan or get a pedicure; do what you need to get rid of any inhibitions. Then you can try stuff to decorate and lick off the body. Feel free to get out a sieve and be creative with cocoa and icing sugar. Can you decorate someone's breasts neatly with strawberry sauce?

47

Get decorating!

If you're not that fussed about new underwear or sex toys, why not try some liquid latex?

You can get really professional and play with the Body Talk Tattoo Set which contains stencils, brushes and chocolate frosting with commands that you can temporarily paint onto the body. And then there's lick-off body gel and body finger paints for you to have fun with. Regular make-up can also be used on body parts; use lip and eye liners to write messages. Another fun game is to appliqué small shells, sequins, sweets, whatever, onto people's bodies using tepid wax. It's a laugh and it gets the fun back. And you need this sense of fun if you want to try out specifically sexual things like new positions, erogenous zones or sex toys.

When we talk about changing, most people imagine a radical change, but taking small steps is enough. Be prepared to try on each other's underwear, or roll around in chocolate sauce and you're pretty much road-tested for anything!

You can buy liquid latex and simply paint it on your body. It's best to shave before applying it (then it's easier to remove), and you can use it to create temporary underwear. Three coats are recommended and each takes around ten minutes to dry. After use, simply peel it off. Imagine the fun you could have decorating each other's bodies!

48

Tie me up, tie me down 2

Create your own bondage chair by tying your partner firmly to a straight backed chair with arms and blindfolding him or her. Or you can order your own bondage chair online.

You don't have to go the whole nine yards to get results. Even on a bog-standard Wednesday night, using your tie, dressing gown belt or whatever happens to be around takes seconds and will add a delicious naughtiness to your love making.

However, half the fun of bondage is that it is unusual so you don't want to make it too mundane. Specialness is heightened if you have an armoury of essential items such as whips, chains, handcuffs and silk scarves hidden away in your boudoir. If you're missing any of this essential paraphernalia then just go online and order your bondage starter kit for less than the price of a dinner for two.

'It would be rude to get your sexual satisfaction by tying someone to the bed and then leaving him or her there and going out with someone more attractive.'

P. J. O'ROURKE

49

Another clichéd (and brilliant) fantasy role play

Bored with naughty nurses, had enough of being disciplined by teacher? Try this one then.

Husband and the Swedish au pair

He is the innocent, she the fun-loving au pair (extra points if she can keep the accent going all the way through). The wife is away and he's settling down to watch the football when she asks if she can join him. Is he seeing things or is her skirt always that short? And is she sitting a little closer than normal? She seems more flirtatious, more brazen. Double meanings and loaded looks are passing between them. He tries to get a grip of himself and resist temptation while she goes out of her way to seduce him into making the first move. Until finally, losing patience, she makes her intentions quite clear...

50

Two final favourite fantasy destinations

A fantasy destination will get your creative juices flowing and some others besides.

Every so often, make one of your dates an at-home soiree. Decide on your fantasy destination – use your imagination and introduce as much role-play as you feel comfortable with.

The camping holiday (your garden, in summer)

You and a friend have gone on a holiday – walking in the hills. After a long day, you set up camp (or settle under the stars in your sleeping bags) in the middle of nowhere. You

switch on a torch, have some dinner, share some jokes, drink some wine, play a game of cards. Before you know it, the game of cards has turned into a strip version of the game and things get very friendly in your tent (or, if you're unperturbed by the neighbours, under the stars)...

Murder in the dark (your house, with the lights off)

You're both guests at a country house party. A fellow guest has suggested a game of murder in the dark. One of you goes off to hide somewhere in the dark silent house. One of you is the murderer who stealthily hunts them down, getting closer and closer. But when the murderer finds the victim, there's another surprise for both of them...

51

Dirty little secrets 2

Try wearing each other's underwear to work.

For women, wearing a loose pair of boxers under a skirt lets the air circulate where it normally never gets to go and makes you feel more open in every sense of the word. For men, the feeling of constriction that comes from tight feminine underwear worn beneath your business suit can be arousing – as well as all the other associations and images that will flash through your mind throughout the day.

Take this one step further and play around with cross-dressing. Wear each other's clothes in bed. You'll hate it or love it, but if you love it, you might be surprised at how much you love it. For men especially, breaking one of the last great heterosexual taboos (dressing as a woman) is a hugely liberating experience. Remember, no one knows but you two.

Need more inspiration? Go to a naturist beach together, make a porn short, photograph each other nude or have sex in the supermarket carpark (make it a quickie!) – risky, but it will give you a little frisson every time you drive to the supermarket!

And, of course, don't break the first rule of secrets. You don't tell. Ever.

52

What you see...

Actively look for images that turn you on and use them in fantasy and lovemaking to make you feel more sexually vibrant.

This is one of the easiest and quickest ways to keep your libido alive and kicking. Wear clothes to bed that turn you on. If you love the way your breasts look in a push-up bra, keep it on. Wear a favourite pair of red stilettos to bed. They may do nothing for him, but you can lie with your feet in the air, admiring what those shoes do for the length of your legs. Love yourself!

This is all easier for women as the sexual female body is a ubiquitous image (and why women find it easy to observe themselves for titillation), but men don't often get the chance to be sex objects. So why not be different? If you really want to rock her world, hire a fireman's outfit for the night. It would be a rare women who wouldn't appreciate the gesture.

Use mirrors – line them up so you can see yourself from all angles. Then experiment with lighting. A torch adds a creepy, otherworldly quality to proceedings and you might find that interesting. It's also hard to get the image of shagging by candlelight out of your mind afterwards, which is a bit less scary and a lot more flattering than a camcorder. Though of course, that works on the same principle.

'We want to know how to turn our mates on. We want them to know what turns us on. We'd like more variety...more foreplay...more surprises...more interest...new tricks...and, once in a while, somebody else should do all the work!'

LAURA CORN

Erotic fantasies is published by Infinite Ideas, publishers of the acclaimed **52 Brilliant Ideas** series. With the **52 Brilliant Ideas** series you can transform your life. You can really improve your performance in or know-how of a subject over the course of a year. Or day. Or month. The choice is yours. There are over 45 titles published in the series over subject areas as diverse as Health & relationships; Sports, hobbies & games; Lifestyle & leisure and Careers, Finance & personal development. Because it's easy once you've got the ideas...

Visit **www.infideas.com** for more information, or e-mail **info@infideas.com**.

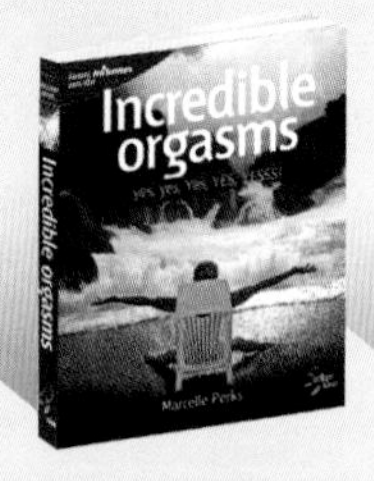

Brilliant sizzling sex series book offer

Exclusive to readers of *Erotic Fantasies* get £2 off another title in our sexy new series

If our authors have tempted you and your partner to try something new in the bedroom why not make bedtime even more fun with another book in the series. *The user's guide to the Rabbit* is the first book to show women and their partners exactly how to get the most out of the world's favourite sex toy. It contains 52 tips from international experts for satisfying yourself and your partner and is the ultimate guide to getting the most out of your Rabbit. So what are you waiting for: order today!

To order your copy of *The user's guide to the Rabbit* at an exclusive discounted price of £4.99 with free p&p (usual price £6.99) simply fill in the form overleaf, cut out or photocopy and send it to Infinite Ideas, 36 St Giles, Oxford OX1 3LD along with a cheque for £4.99.*

Alternatively visit **www.infideas.com** and enter promotional code **'Rabbit52'** at the checkout. Your discount will be applied automatically.

*Please note that no payment will be taken until your purchase has been dispatched.

Name:...

Delivery address:..

....

....

....

Email:...

Telephone:...

Offer code: Rabbit52